The I LOVE MY BODY BOOK

by Lisa Lynn

© 2015 Lisa Lynn
Art by Toby Mikle of
MyBookIllustrator.com

To: K and K
Love, Mommy

I love my legs because they let me run fast.

I love my arms because they let me hug my family.

I love my eyes
because they
let me see
beautiful things.

I love
my mouth
because it
lets me smile
BIG.

I love my ears because they let me hear happy sounds.

I love my nose because it lets me smell delicious smells (like brownies).

I love my lips because they let me give kisses to my dog.

I love my heart because it helps me to LOVE.

I love my stomach because it holds my food inside my body so I can play all day!

I love my mind because it allows me to daydream.

I love my skin
because it
protects me
from the sun.

I love my hands because they let me hold things tight.

I love my feelings because
they allow me to
FEEL changes in
my body or my
mood.

I love my appetite because it keeps my body nourished.

I love my brain because it allows me to learn.

I love my voice
because it
lets me say
"I LOVE YOU"!

I love my personality because it makes me who I am.

I love my soul
because it
allows me to
believe in
GOD

We all need to learn to love our bodies exactly the way GOD made them.

Most of all we
need to be
grateful for
what our bodies
let us do
every day.

Remember to
HONOR GOD
WITH YOUR
BOD by:

And to always follow your heart — it knows where it's going!

We all need to feel loved.

Remember to LOVE yourself!

And most of all,
remember
that GOD LOVES
YOU EXACTLY THE
WAY YOU ARE!

In His eyes you are
perfect!

Made in the USA
Middletown, DE
13 July 2015